HIS NAME WAS QUINCY

BY

KEISHA GREEN

ILLUSTRATIONS BY JOSIAN RODRIQUEZ

Published by Keisha Green of JDX Publishing Company, LLC., Cornwall, New York

Book Coach – The Self-Publishing Maven
Formatting – Manuel Quintana
Illustrations – Josian Rodriquez
Proofreading – Robin Devonish

ISBN 13: 978-1-7353345-0-9

Printed in the United States of America

www.jdxpublishingcompanyllc.com

I dedicate this book to my three reasons why, Jahmir, Diamond and Xavier (JDX). You are EXACTLY what the world needs. You have limitless potential. You are smart, courageous, kind, driven, ambitious, purposeful, bold, invaluable and wonderfully made in God's eyes. The world doesn't dictate who you are; YOUR CHARACTER dictates who you are. Always, always, always take up space, unapologetically and don't allow anyone to ever dull your sparkle.
K.L.G.M

HIS NAME WAS QUINCY

BY

KEISHA GREEN

Every night mama and I say our prayers.

She tells me it's important we pray so God can keep us safe.

So every night we pray.

One morning I heard mama and daddy yelling and crying. So I jumped out of bed to see what all the fuss was about.

Mama's cry somehow sounded different and I knew something wasn't right.

He's dead! He's dead!

I can't believe they took my baby from me.

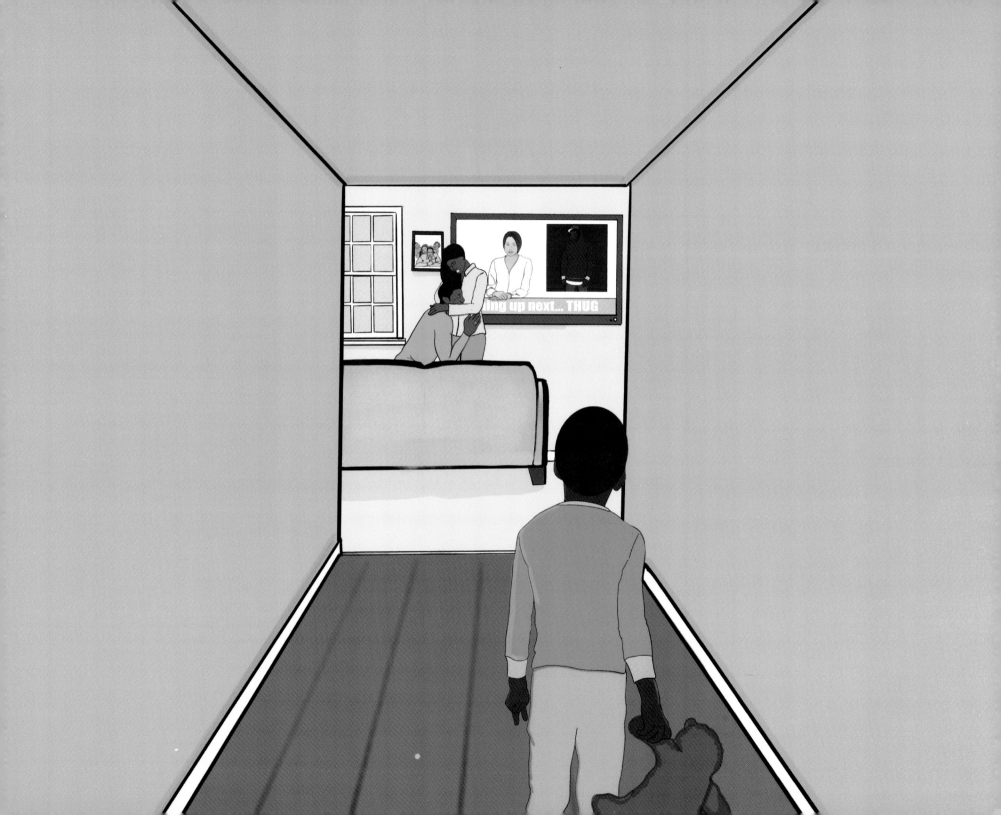

On the TV sat my older brother's picture.

He didn't quite look the same. That's not how I knew my brother Quincy.

It was a younger picture of Quincy but it was DEFINITELY Quincy.

There he was, my brother Quincy standing in the middle of two friends.

One friend had both hands in his pocket. Quincy had his hands folded as if he were about to pray. His other friend had his hands folded across his chest.

None of them were smiling. The words under their picture read, THUG.

My head tilted to the side in wonder trying to figure out, what the word THUG meant and why would Quincy be on TV in that photo?

We had so many other photos of Quincy.

Like the one when he graduated from high school, or the one when he got his college acceptance letter, or his latest picture when he graduated from college, or perhaps my personal favorite, the one when he was holding me when I was born.

Daddy held Mama tight and they rocked back and forth.

I stood alone quiet, frozen, and unsure of what to do.

I held on to the words momma moaned earlier. Slowly and silently repeating them in my head.
He's dead! He's dead!

So many questions left unanswered.
Who's dead?
How did they die?
What does the word *THUG* mean?
Why is Quincy on TV in a picture that was barely recognizable to me?

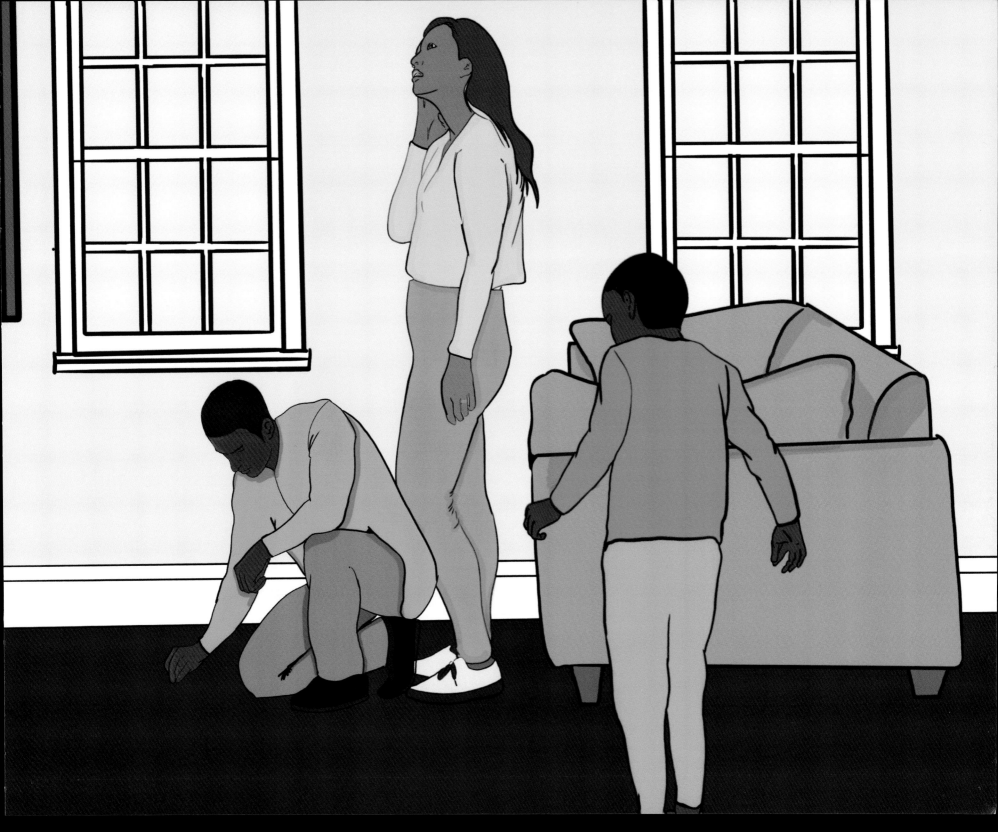

I tiptoed over unsure of what to do.

Mama with bloodshot red eyes and tears streaming down her face grabbed me tight and said, "Baby Quincy is gone."

I felt something rise in the pit of my stomach, and just like mama, I exploded into tears.

Mama, Daddy and I huddled close, our pain engulfed in our huddle unwilling to be set free.

What the world would never know about Quincy was that *HE* was my big brother.

***He* was my *HERO*.**

He just celebrated his 21st birthday the same day he graduated from college.

Him and mama loved to garden. Peonies were his favorite.

His favorite color was blue. It reminded him of the ocean.

He sang alto in our church choir.

He was the lead in his high school play.

He loved to take me to the park where I would ride my bike.

He taught me how to cradle the ball for lacrosse.

He also taught me how to do butterfly kicks in the pool.

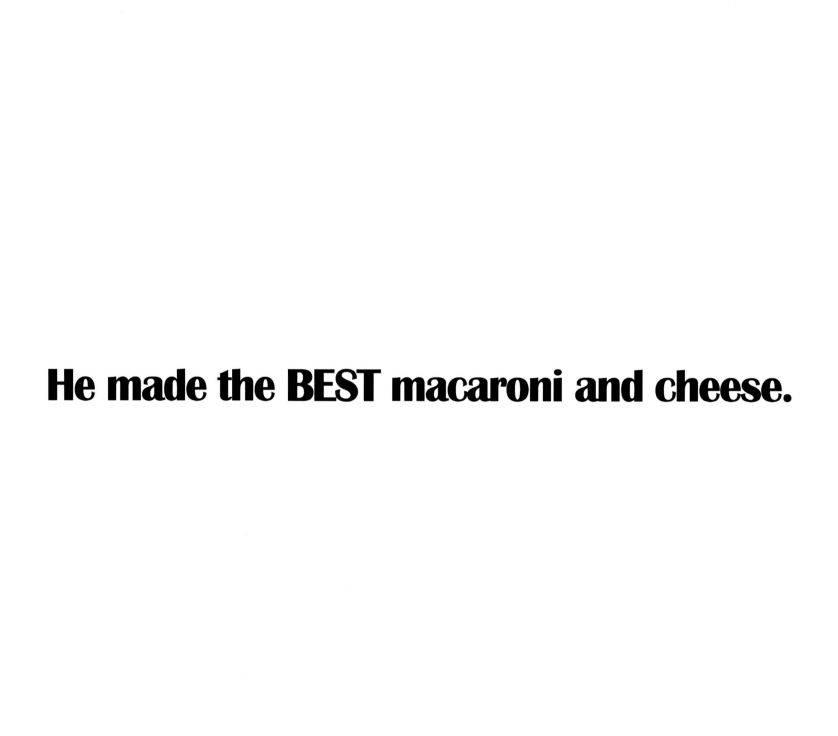

He made the BEST macaroni and cheese.

Last night Quincy left home to celebrate his new job at some big advertising firm.

Mama and Daddy were so proud and I could tell Quincy was too.

If I had known that Quincy wouldn't make it back home, last night when we prayed I would have asked God to tell the people on TV his name was Quincy and not THUG.

Now I know why they chant, SAY HIS NAME.

About the Illustrator

Josian Rodriguez was born in Mayaguez, Puerto Rico and moved to New York City in the early 90's. Being introduced to art at an early age by his family, he developed a love for sketching, and painting. He graduated with a M.B.A from Mercy College and has been a Special Education Technology teacher for 9 years. HIs appreciation of technology in the classroom has further established a passion for all types of representations of Art. Currently in the field education and consulting for 16 years he has the opportunity to work with different school districts across the nation. Mr. Rodriquez has mentored and collaborated with teachers on project based learning curricula while incorporating art, dance, music, film and technology. Josian Rodriguez can be contacted at JRagencyinmotion@gmail.com.